TOMORROW I WILL FEEL BETTER

Illustrations: Ann de Bode
Original title: *Morgen ben ik weer beter*
© Van In, Lier, 1995. Van In Publishers, Grote Markt 39,
2500 Lier, Belgium.
© in this edition Evans Brothers Limited 1997
(world English rights excluding the USA and Canada)
English text by Su Swallow

First published in paperback in 1999

First published in Great Britain by
Evans Brothers Limited
2A Portman Mansions
Chiltern Street
London W1M 1LE

Printed by KHL (Singapore)

0 237 52044 3

HELPING HANDS

TOMORROW I WILL FEEL BETTER

ANN DE BODE AND RIEN BROERE

Evans

Evans Brothers Limited

For Kim

The doctor is sitting on Rosie's bed.
Something is wrong with her heart.
So tomorrow she is going into hospital.
The doctor will make her heart better.
'Would you like to listen?' the doctor asks.
So Rosie listens.
She can hear her heart going 'pfft, pfft'.
It sounds like a bicycle pump, she thinks.

Rosie packs her bag for tomorrow.
She puts in all the things she wants to take.
Lots of books and toys,
and coloured crayons.
Her brother and sister have drawn pictures for her.
Teddy doesn't understand what is going on.
'Stay close to me, Teddy,' she says.
'And don't worry. Tomorrow I will feel better.'

Rosie is very proud of her new pyjamas.
Mum has made them for her.
The top has lots of little buttons,
so it opens easily and
the doctor can look at her chest.
Teddy is very proud too.
He's got the same pyjamas as Rosie,
and a little nightcap to match.

At the hospital, a nurse comes to look after Rosie.
Rosie thinks she's very nice.
She tells Rosie what is going to happen.
Then Rosie tells Teddy.
'Look what a big bed I've got,' she says.
'And it's got wheels.
We're going for a ride down the corridor soon,
and you're coming with me!'

Rosie's mum sleeps in the same room as Rosie.
She has a magic bed.
First it's a chair, then Mum says, 'Abracadabra!'
She pulls a lever and hey presto,
the chair turns into a bed.
'We could swap beds,' says Rosie.
'That would give the doctors a fright!'
But her bed is too small for her mum.

Rosie doesn't like the nurse all the time.
When the nurse needs a little blood,
she has to put a needle into Rosie's arm.
Rosie tries to be brave,
but she feels cross and cries a bit.
You wait, she thinks.
I shall tell Teddy about this.

The nurse fixes a small tube to Rosie's arm.
The tube goes into a small bag
which hangs on a stand on wheels.
Rosie is so brave that the nurse
brings her a big box of toys to choose from.

Here's the nurse again.
And she's brought something else.
Will I get another present? wonders Rosie.
It's a bracelet.
It has Rosie's name on it,
and the number of her room.
Teddy gets a bracelet, too, of course.
They will keep them on until they go home.

'Come along,' says Mum.
'Let me put your hair in bunches.'
'Why?' asks Rosie.
'So your hair doesn't get tangled while
you're asleep,' says Mum.
'There, you look beautiful.' She gives Rosie a big kiss.
Rosie can see that her mum is trying not to cry,
so she gives her a big hug.

'I'm going to give you an injection,' says the nurse.
'It will make you fall sound asleep.'
'If you give me an injection on my bottom,
only my bottom will go to sleep!' cries Rosie.
Mum laughs. 'Try blowing out hard,
then you will hardly feel a thing.'

Rosie's bed is wheeled down the corridor.
Mum and the nurse walk beside her.
This is fun, thinks Rosie.
And Teddy enjoys the ride too.
In another room they meet some people all in green.
Mum gives Rosie a big, big kiss.
Rosie wants to say something,
but she just can't keep her eyes open.

The doctors will make Rosie's heart better.
She won't see or feel anything
because she's asleep.
But when she wakes up afterwards
her heart will be better
and she will be able to play with her friends.
Teddy stays very close to her,
so nothing can go wrong.

Slowly Rosie starts to wake up.
She can hear music in the distance. Or a bell.
And people whispering.
Mum says, 'I love you.' Dad says, 'Me too.'
Rosie feels dizzy. Is it afternoon or evening?
When can I go home? she wonders.
She can go home soon, but first she must
rest in hospital, and take lots of medicines.

There's a long scar on Rosie's chest.
The doctor has put a big plaster on it.
There are two more plasters on her tummy.
And two tiny tubes.
Teddy has some plasters, too.
Doctor Rosie put those on.

When Rosie wants to go to the toilet,
she has to stay in bed.
The nurse brings her a funny pot
called a bedpan.
It feels very cold,
but Rosie manages.

Three times a day, the nurse
puts a band round Rosie's arm
and pumps air into it.
This is to check her blood pressure.
And three times a day, the nurse
takes Rosie's temperature.
This is to check that she doesn't have a fever.
Goodness, what a fuss they are making of her!

Lots of doctors come to see Rosie.
They want to know if everything is fine,
and they talk to Rosie's mum.
They use words that Rosie doesn't understand.
Mum smiles and hugs her.
'You're doing fine, little one,' she says, and cries a little.
'I love you, Mum,' says Rosie,
and gives her a big kiss.

Rosie has been in hospital for
quite a long time now.
She's even made a new friend, called Lucy.
When the doors are open they
can see each other.
They wave and call out.
Rosie is getting better,
and the tubes have been taken out.

Sometimes Rosie gets out of bed.
Just for a little while. The scar pulls a bit,
and her skin feels tight.
But no more pyjamas!
'You can choose what to wear,' says Mum.
Rosie goes for a ride in a pushchair.
Teddy goes too, of course.

It's lunchtime.
'I'm not hungry,' says Rosie.
I don't want anything to eat.'
Mum makes a face on her plate,
but Rosie still isn't hungry.
'Have a drink, then,' says Mum.
'Then try to eat something.'
'I wish I could have some sweets,' sighs Rosie.

'Come into the kitchen with me,' says the nurse.
'You can choose what you want to eat.'
'I'm not hungry,' Rosie says.
'Wait a minute,' says another nurse.
She finds a pot of creamy yoghurt.
But Rosie doesn't touch it.
She really doesn't feel like eating anything.

Every day a lady comes to see Rosie.
She wants to check Rosie's breathing.
Rosie calls it the tickling hour,
because the lady has a funny machine
which tickles. Rosie has to blow into
the machine and make bubbles in the water.
Lots of bubbles. As many as she can.

It's night-time. There's hardly a sound.
But Rosie can be heard crying quietly.
She's missing her dad, and her brother and sister.
'Come into my bed for a cuddle,' her mum whispers.
So Rosie climbs in and snuggles up.
The nurse jumps when she sees Rosie's bed is empty.
That makes Rosie and her mum laugh.

Rosie has had a lot of cards.
There are cards from her schoolfriends
and her teacher, and from her aunts
and uncles and all the neighbours.
Too many to count. Rosie has put them up
on the wall above her bed.
She often looks at them.
They cheer her up a lot.

Rosie gets lots of visitors.
Uncle Frank and Auntie Pauline came.
And Auntie Chris, and James, and many others.
They bring lots of little presents.
'You're a very brave little girl,' they tell her.
Rosie likes seeing everybody,
but she still gets tired very quickly.

There's a little school in the hospital.
Now that Rosie is feeling better,
she can go there for a while every day.
The teacher is very kind.
Rosie cuts and sticks and draws.
She hangs the best pictures at the end of her bed.

Rosie has her picture taken.
But it's no ordinary picture.
It shows her lungs and her heart.
The doctors can check that they are working properly.
They look at the picture on a television screen.
Rosie and Teddy have a look too.
It's funny to see what's going on inside you.

The nurse comes to take Rosie's plasters off.
She tells Rosie to blow hard again,
to stop it hurting too much.
It does hurt a bit, but Rosie is very brave.
Then Nurse Rosie takes Teddy's plaster off too.
He is as brave as Rosie,
so she gives him a big kiss.

Now all you can see on Rosie's chest
is a long pink scar. It goes from top to bottom.
Mum puts cream on it every day.
'Soon it will fade until it's just
a thin white line,' she says.
And Rosie's brother says, 'If the scar wasn't there,
you wouldn't be there either!'
And he's quite right.

The doctor comes.
'Listen to your heart,' he says.
Rosie listens. It goes 'boom, boom, boom'.
'It sounds like a drum,' she says.
'That means it's fine,' says the doctor.
'Tomorrow, you can go home.'
Rosie is very happy. But first,
she draws a nice picture for the doctor.

Rosie gets ready to go home. She takes all her cards
with her, and her clothes, and all the presents.
Teddy is going home, too, of course.
The case will hardly shut.
At home there's a big party for Rosie,
with a huge chocolate cake.
There's plenty for everyone,
and even Snoopy the dog gets a slice!